D1107636

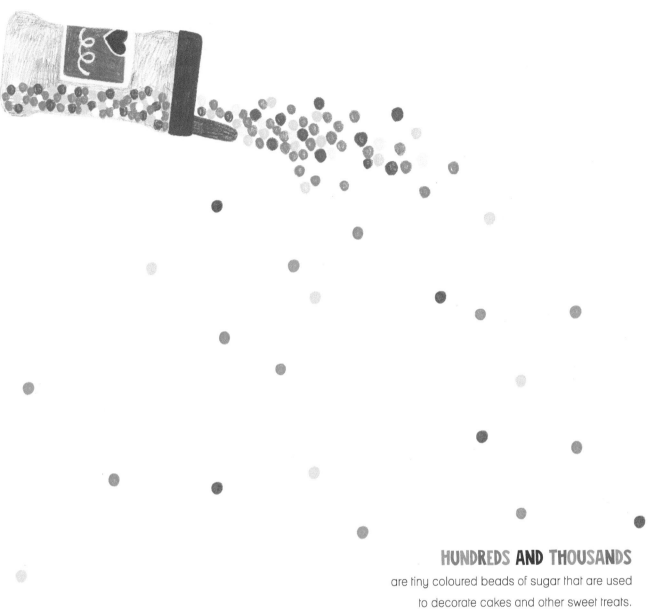

## HUNDREDS **AND THOUSANDS**

are tiny coloured beads of sugar that are used
to decorate cakes and other sweet treats.
In some parts of the world they are also called
*sprinkles* or *nonpareils*.

The term **HUNDREDS AND THOUSANDS**
is used to describe a **SUPER LARGE** but not
specific number of something – like when you
have lots and lots and lots of something but
you're not exactly sure how much you have.

**SO** if someone loves you hundreds and thousands
it means they love you *soooooo* much –
more than anybody could ever count...

Bookalicious
PUBLISHING

# We love you HUNDREDS AND THOUSANDS

*Dara Read*

For **FINN** and **KAIA**,
our beautiful babes...

and to my parents and birth parents,
*thank you*

I **LOVE** birthday parties,
especially my own!

I don't always have a birthday cake,
but I **ALWAYS**
have hundreds and thousands.

One year, Mum and Dad
made a massive slip-and-slide.

My friends and I

# SLIPPED

and

# SLID

all over the place.

We
LAUGHED
so hard my face hurt!

I had a fairy bread cake
made with layers of fluffy
white bread covered in
hundreds and thousands.

We ended up with
RAINBOW
FRECKLES
all over our faces.

'Where does Jasmine get all her energy from?'
Mum asked Dad as we rolled up the plastic after the party.

'Not from me!'
he said.

And I said,
'But you love
me hundreds
and thousands.'

The next year I had
a sleepover.
My friends arrived in
their **PYJAMAS**.
Mum put up a huge
tent in the backyard.

We drank **HOT CHOCOLATE**...

...and stayed up until **MIDNIGHT**

ooooooh

telling ghost stories...

...around the **FIRE**.

I had a **MARSHMALLOW** cake covered in hundreds and thousands.

We toasted the marshmallows on the fire.

The hundreds and thousands

melted

...making a

# RAINBOW
## MESS.

'Where does Jasmine get her love of the outdoors from?'
Dad asked Mum as we packed up the tent after the party.

'Not from me!'
she said.

nd I said,
But you love
ne hundreds
nd thousands.'

Last year, I had a

# DISCO PARTY.

Dad covered the lights a

indows in the living room with RED, **YELLOW** and **BLUE** cellophane.

...and sang at the

TOP

OF          OUR

LUNGS!

I had an **ICE CREAM CAKE** covered in hundreds and thousands.

We **LICKED** the hundreds and thousands off the top of the cake...

...before eating the rest
with a **SPOON**.

'Where does she get her rhythm from?' Dad asked Mum as we took down the cellophane after the party.

'Not from me!'
she said.

And I said,
'But you love
me hundreds
and thousands.'

People say to me,
'You look so
much like
your Mum!'

They say,
'You and
your Dad
are like
two peas
in a pod.'

I think it's funny because I didn't **GROW** in Mum's tummy.

Not everyone knows this about me.
The ones who do know like to ask me
HUNDREDS AND THOUSANDS
OF QUESTIONS ABOUT IT.

It's pretty simple really. My birth parents made
me, and **Mum** and **Dad** grew me up.

Mum says to me,
'You grew in my heart,
not under it.'

This makes me feel
**SUPER** special.

One day I'd **LOVE** my birth parents
to come to my birthday party.

Everyone could sing
happy birthday together...

...and then
Mum and Dad
would say what they
always say...

We
love you

HUNDREDS
AND
THOUSANDS!

Who loves **YOU** hundreds
and thousands?

Draw them here
and keep them in your heart *forever*.

# THE AUTHOR

Dara was born in Australia in the 80s and
was adopted by her mum and dad who
love parties as much as she does.
Did we mention that Dara loves parties?
She does, especially if she can dance!

When Dara met her birth parents and their
families, she danced for joy - on the inside!

Dara now lives by the beach in Sydney
with her family. Her favourite things are
cuddles with her kids, being in the ocean
and almost anything that sparkles.

On the more serious side, Dara is a writer
and social justice lawyer. She has worked
as a children's lawyer and youth worker.
She has also been a senior ministerial
adviser for children who are adopted and
in out-of-home care.

The author would like to thank
*everyone* who encouraged and
supported this book into being,
including Nicky, Kelly, Erin, Yo,
Jane and Rachel.

She would **especially** like to thank
Andrew, Robs and Daria
from the bottom of her heart.

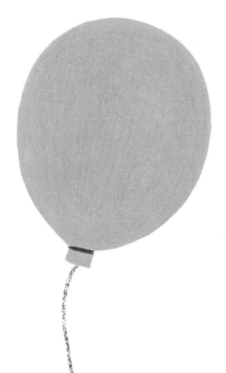

Published in Australia by Bookalicious Publishing
PO box 4049, Maroubra South 2035
dara.read@gmail.com
www.dararead.com

First published in Australia in 2021

Copyright © Dara Read 2020

 A catalogue record for this
book is available from the
National Library of Australia

ISBN: 978-0-6488195-0-9 (paperback)
ISBN:  978-0-6488195-1-6 (hardback)
ISBN: 978-0-6488195-2-3 (epub)

Illustrations by Daria Solak
Cover formatted by Rachel Kaiserblueth, Kaisermelon Designs
Art Direction, Typography and Finished Art by Rachel Kaiserblueth, Kaisermelon Designs

Printed by Ingram Spark

CPSIA information can be obtained
at www.ICGtesting.com
Printed in the USA
LVHW071549261021
701599LV00001B/26